THE LEGENDARY ADVENTURES OF THE

Flying Mingling Brothers

Pictures and Stories by

Jamie Hayes

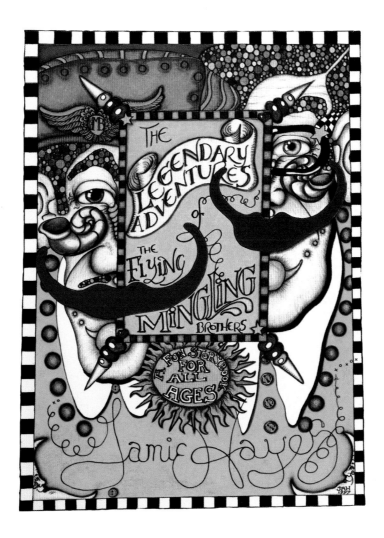

Bubba One Publishing Co.

New Orleans, Louisiana

To
Michael S. Clanton,
a.k.a. Bubba
R.I.P.
My dear friend, I miss you so.

To Pamela and Julian,
who helped me with this book in
ways they'll never know.

And a special thanks to
Theodore A. Rees Cheney,
Feargal Padraig Conway and Pramote Jamsrikaew
who helped make these stories and
book so presentable.

New Jacket/Cover Art and Design: Jamie Hayes
Copyeditor: Theodore A. Rees Cheney
Original Book Design and Production : Jamie Hayes

ISBN : 0-9661213-0-9

Second Edition
5,000 copies

Printed at 21st Century Printing
Bangkok,10700
Kingdom of Thailand

2015

AMOS and OBI

CHAPTERS

Welcome to the Worlds of.....

"How do you like my party hat, boys? Didn't you know cruise boats are way too heavy to float on their own?"

Cruzhead Jack

"Help," Bubba screamed, "I'm falling!" But it was too late. A big wave and a little too much fun after dinner made him lose his balance. Even before he hit the water, the other Bubba leaped over the railing after his best friend.

"I'm comin' to save ya, Bubba!" he yelled out. They hit the water moments apart and in the darkness completely lost their orientation. "Uh-oh," they thought. Suddenly something very big grabbed them.

"Don't be afraid," a friendly voice said. "My name is Cruzhead Jack, one of the sea people. Fortunately, I saw you when you fell into the water."

The two Bubbas were confused. They usually accepted almost anything that happened, but this was too much. They were looking into the eyes of a **giant!** Lucky for them, they were kind eyes, and the big fellow was smiling from ear to ear.

"Hello, sir," one of the Bubbas finally said. "We're the Flying Mingling Brothers, and I guess we fell overboard. I shouldn't have been walking along the ship's railing. Oh yes, by the way, my name is Bubba."

"And mine is too!" the other Bubba chimed in. Somehow, they felt absolutely no fear of this friendly giant.

"Hello Bubbas!" said Cruzhead Jack with a huge smile. "Welcome to my world! Would you like to stay for a visit? Not many land people drop in, so I would love to show you around."

"Why, sure! You don't have to ask the Flying Mingling Brothers twice about going on a trip," one Bubba said.

"We're with you and ready," replied the other Bubba.

Holding the boys in the palm of his hand, Cruzhead Jack placed them gently onto his shoulders. They were off on what turned out to be one of the Flying Mingling Brothers' most memorable adventures. That first night, the fun began.

As the trio started moving, the boys looked up and saw their cruise boat on top of the giant's head. Cruzhead Jack saw them looking up and asked, "How do you like my party hat, boys? Didn't you know that cruise boats are much too heavy to float on their own, so the sea people work underneath the big ships to make sure they stay afloat?"

"Really...?" The two Bubbas looked amazed.

"Yes, and not to change the subject, but have you two ever heard of the Golden Tree?" Cruzhead Jack asked.

"No, I don't think so, Jack," one Bubba said, the other Bubba shaking his head. "What is it?"

"Tonight must be your lucky night," Cruzhead Jack. Not only are you getting to see the sea world, you're also going to get three wishes!" The boys grew excited as Cruzhead Jack continued. "In a little while, we're going to come up on the Golden Tree under the sea. You must close your eyes when I tell you, and under no circumstances, look at the Golden Tree. I'll go around the tree three times, one time for each wish. If you do not even peek, your wishes will come true." The boys were as happy as could be. A while later, Cruzhead Jack whispered, "This is it boys, close your eyes. We're comin' up on the Golden Tree. Don't forget to make your wishes!"

The two Bubbas did as they were told, when suddenly the most beautiful golden light glowed inside their heads and even though their eyes were closed, they could clearly see the Golden Tree. Slowly, the light faded, and then they could hear Cruzhead Jack whisper again.

"Get some sleep boys. you must be tired. Good night and sleep tight, Bubbas. See you tomorrow..."

The boys fell into the most glorious sleep they had ever experienced. They spent the night dreaming of what they had wished.

Saint Augen Zauber is always busy
hypnotizing fish.

Saint Augen Zauber
(The saint with the magic eyes)

Readers may have heard of the popular saints like the Irish Saint Patrick, Saint Christopher, Saint John, Saint Nicholas, and Saint Mary; but one saint goes largely unknown. The patron saint of all fish, Saint Augen Zauber.

One fine day, the Flying Mingling Brothers were travelling with Cruzhead Jack when they saw a whole school of fish swimming vertically straight up and down. Just when the boys were going to ask about them, Cruzhead Jack made a very sharp turn and walked right through the vertical column of fish.

"Hey, Bubbas," he whispered, "there's someone over here I'd like you to meet. He's a very good friend of mine who's an even better friend of fish." "Hello, Augen Zauber," Cruzhead Jack said to the very busy-looking man. As they were approaching him, the man was "zapping" school after school of fish with his eyes. Everytime he looked at the fish, they began swimming up and down.

"Hello, Cruzhead Jack! I'd love to chat, but the fishing season started today. As you can see, I'm very, very busy saving fish." Just as Saint Augen Zauber said that, another group of horizontal fish suddenly went vertical.

"Saint Augen, I know how busy you are and I promise not to interrupt your work for long, but I have some new friends I'd like to introduce you to." Cruzhead Jack pointed at the Double Bubbas on his shoulders. "These are the Flying Mingling Brothers, Bubba and Bubba. Bubba to the left and Bubba to the right."

For just a moment, Saint Augen looked up into the Bubbas' eyes and said,

"Hello and hello to the two of you, Bubba and Bubba! I'd love to chat, but I must be on my way, I am very busy today saving fish. May you both be blessed, and good luck!" As he said that, the boys started to tingle all over with an uncontrollable desire to stand up on Cruzhead Jack's shoulder.

"Saint Augen Zauber is the busiest guy I know," Cruzhead Jack said. "he's always saving his beloved fish. By the way, do fishermen know about him?"

"No," the boys answered with a guilty conscience, "I don't think so."

"On days when fishermen are fishing and don't catch anything," Cruzhead Jack explained, "it's probably not the result of bad luck. More than likely it's Saint Augen Zauber hypnotizing fish nearby. It's impossible to catch a vertically swimming fish. They just go up and down, up and down, looking at the hooks as they go by them."

"How 'bout that!" The two Bubbas said, then looked at each other and grew quieter. They felt a little guilty because back home they did love to fish. Of course they had left out that little detail about themselves during their encounter with Saint Augen Zauber.

From then on, the two Bubbas always laughed when their fishing buddies returned from a bad day of fishing. If they only knew...

The Pucker Fish

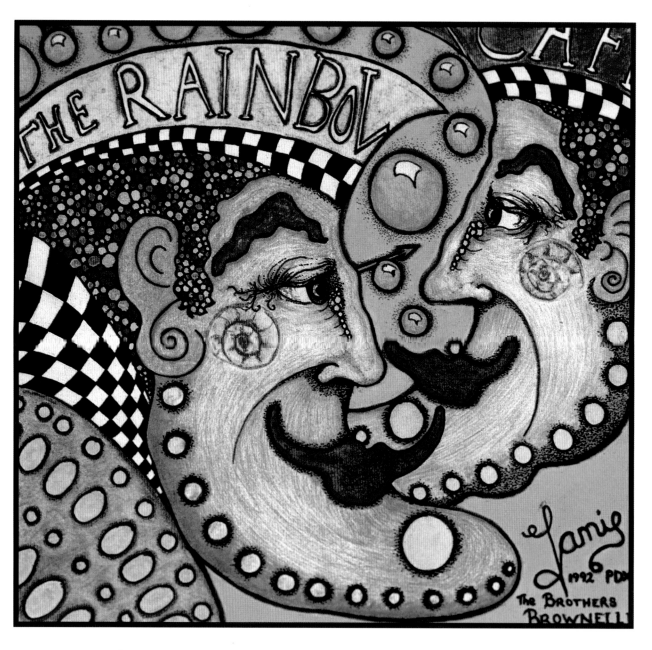

The waiters at the Rainbow Cafe
are required to paint their faces blue.

The Rainbow Cafe

"I'm starving!" said one of the Bubbas.

"Me too!" said the other.

"No problem," said Cruzhead Jack. "Look, right over there is the Rainbow Cafe. They serve up great food, and it's really a fun place too. Let's go!" Cruzhead Jack didn't even wait for the boys to answer.

They were greeted at the door by a blue-faced maitre'd, who seated the Double Bubbas at a large round table, with lots of napkins and guests. He tied an oversized bib onto everybody and said. "Welcome to the Rainbow Cafe. Your waiter, one of the Brownelli Brothers, will be right with you." Then he disappeared.

The two bubbas looked around the table and smiled, "Hello everybody, I'm Bubba and this is my best friend whose name is Bubba also. We're the Flying Mingling Brothers."

There were "hello's" and introductions all around. Everyone was in fine spirits. Without ordering, the food came and it was delicious. The portions were way oversized, and the boys wondered why they were served so much.

Mr. Brownelli was the most efficient waiter the boys had ever seen, and his face, too, was painted blue. All the waiters that worked in

Rainbow Cafe were required to paint their faces blue. They also wore plastic hats and uniforms with "Rainbow Cafe" printed on them. Unfortunately the blue face-paint made all the waiters look alike, so it was impossible to tell which waiter was yours. After everyone had finished eating as much as they could, the waiters snuck up on the customers and painted their faces blue too. It happened so quickly that the boys didn't get a chance to object, although they wouldn't have anyway. They looked around the table and everybody's face was blue. Without warning, one Bubba was hit right smack in the middle of his forehead with a handful of noodles. A moment later a glob of "secret sauce" hit the other Bubba right smack in his eye. They looked at each other in complete surprise and smiled. Then they grabbed handfuls of whatever they could and flung it at the blue-faced smart-alecks who had thrown first.

"GOTCHA!"said Bubba.

"FOOD FIGHT, FOOD FIGHT," yelled everyone at the table.The place went completely berserk. Food was airborne and it was the wildest thing the boys had ever seen. Everybody screamed, laughed, and threw food at the same time. The Flying Mingling Brothers were right in the thick of it, holding their own.Those excellent waiters kept on serving and replacing food the whole time, so there was plenty of ammunition to go around.

"What a fun restaurant," the two Bubbas said to Cruzhead Jack, simultaneously smashing him in the face with a gigantic, incredibly messy chocolate pie. After the food fight had gone on long enough, everyone was given lots of clean-up towels and little buckets of water. Afterwards they shook hands all around, complimented each other on the particularly good shots, and then said goodnight.

The Rainbow Cafe is the Flying Mingling Brothers' favorite restaurant of all time.

The coolest king that ever was.

King Delectable

The sea people breathe differently than land people. Always surrounded by bubbles, they breathe in seawater and somehow when they inhale turn it into air. They breathe out the air bubbles, which rise to the top and provide us land dwellers with air. That is why it is so important for us to keep our rivers, lakes, and oceans really clean. The sea people need the purest water to produce clean fresh air.

King Delectable, the king of the sea, may be the coolest king there ever was. The way he becomes king is very simple. Every year or two, the citizens hold a contest and whoever makes them laugh the loudest, becomes king. For as long as anyone can remember, the same person has always won, - King Delectable. He is a very funny fellow and an especially clever songwriter. King Delectable always composes a new little ditty every year for the big competition.

The Flying Mingling Brothers were two very lucky guys, because they arrived in the sea world just in time for that year's coronation. An extravagant event, the show turned out to be the funniest thing the two Bubbas had ever experienced. Each contestant auditioning for the job of king, had five minutes to make the crowd laugh. There was a gigantic applause meter sitting on the stage which registered the volume level. Each act was funnier then the one before, and everybody was having a great time.

Following tradition, the king came to the stage last. Everyone in the crowd was already trying hard not to laugh. Some people even pinched themselves in an effort not to laugh. When King Delectable walked on the stage, he was completely encompassed by bubbles. He had loads and loads more bubbles than anyone else. The King was also a chili fanatic. In fact, it was the only thing he ate during coronation week. Chef R.U.A. Bean, the king's personal chef, cooked up only chili concoctions and on Coronation Day, the chef dumped into the chili way more beans than usual. King Delectable came on stage and started strumming his little yellow ukulele and began slowly to sing this song:

Beans, beans, the musical fruit,
the more you eat,
the more you toot.
Toot, tootin' all day...
Singing, toodle, oodle, oodle, oodle...
Toot, tootin all day.

Tears rolled down the Double Bubbas faces and the crowd howled uncontrollably, as more and more bubbles appeared from behind the king. The needle on the applause meter went right off the scale, so once again King Delectable remained king for another year. Unfortunately, after the coronation the King was whisked away in his amazing under-water limousine before the two Bubbas could meet him. They did get a chance to meet his personal chef, R.U.A. Bean. He was kind enough to offer the Bubbas one of his famous chili recipes. It is absolutely delectable and really easy to make. Try it yourself.

King Delectable's Chili

2 pounds ground beef chuck

1 pound ground pork

3 tablespoons bacon fat

3 medium onions

4 cloves of garlic, minced

1 - 28-oz. can of crushed tomatoes

2 -16 oz. cans of kidney beans (the musical fruit)

1 tablespoon chili powder

1 tablespoon oregano

1 teaspoon cumin

2 bay leaves, crushed

salt and pepper to taste

tomato juice or beef broth, as needed

optional: cayenne pepper, hot sauce, or minced jalepeño pepper

2 cups shredded Monterey Jack cheese

1 cup shredded sharp cheddar cheese

Quickly sear ground beef and pork in bacon fat over high heat.
Lower heat and sauté onions and garlic along with meat until they are
golden. Add tomatos, beans and seasonings. Simmer uncovered over very
low heat for 2 hours. If sauce becomes too thick, add tomato juice or beef

broth. To make sauce even spicier add cayenne pepper, hot sauce, or minced jalepeño pepper.

Line a 4-quart casserole dish with 1/2 of the cheese. Fill the casserole with chili, and top with remaining cheese. Bake in a preheated 375 - degree oven for about 25 minutes, or until cheese is bubbly and golden brown. Serve with tortilla chips. Yum!

Author's note: The Bubbas sometimes use a short cut version of this recipe. They buy their favorite canned chili, dump it in a casserole dish and skip right to the part about baking it with cheese for 25 minutes.

(Please don't tell chef R.U.A. Bean the Double Bubbas do that.)

Bubba's Big Surprise

The Flying Mingling Brothers rarely argued. One day, however, while sitting in the Rainbow Cafe, they were having a loud discussion. It was about an "unexplainable purchase" one of the Bubbas had made. They somehow always made ends meet and had enough left over to buy just about anything they wanted. At this moment though, their situation was looking bleak. The Double Bubbas were broke and arguing about money. Almost unnoticeably a calm voice interrupted their little spat.

"Will there be anything else, boys?" asked their blue-faced waiter, Mr. Brownelli. He really liked the Flying Mingling Brothers and somehow sensed their financial woes. "Hey boys, don't worry, be happy. Lunch is on the house today. You can tip me double next time!" he said with a big, blue- faced smile and a bluish wink. One of the boys leaned a little closer to him and said quietly, "Gee, thanks so much Mr. Brownelli, we'll pay you double next time, we promise." Once outside, there was still tension between them. To avoid further disagreement, one of the Bubbas says, "meet me here tomorrow at two o'clock. I'm outta here," and stormed off.

"Okay then," said the other. They headed their separate ways. They each had but one thing on their mind, MONEY. The Flying Mingling Brothers were usually masters of the quick buck, but this time they were having no luck at all. Before one of the Bubbas knew it, it was approaching two o'clock the next day and still nothing. "Gee," he thought,

"I wonder if Bubba had more success than I did?" He had hoped to return with a pocket full of money and a good mood, but when he walked back into the Rainbow Cafe, he was moping.

"SURPRISE!!!!!!!" The chorus rang out from all over the restaurant. The place was packed with all their friends. He'd been so caught up in their financial crisis, he'd forgotten that it was his birthday. Everybody was there. Cruzhead Jack, Uncle Iggy, Gustavo and Erica, King Delectable, and even Saint Augen Zauber with some of his fish friends. Bubba was looking around for Bubba when he saw in the middle of the dining room, the biggest chocolate birthday cake he'd ever seen. He felt really guilty. "How silly of me," he thought, "of course, this party is Bubba's unexplainable purchase." He was feeling really bad, when suddenly the giant cake flew apart and out popped good ol' Bubba.

"HAPPY BIRTHDAY, BUBBA!" he yelled out with a chocolate covered smile. Everybody joined in singing avery loud rendition of the "HAPPY BIRTHDAY," song to BUBBA!

"Wow, thank you everybody, I don't know what to say." He looked over toward his best friend. "Thank you with all my heart, Bubba. This is the best birthday party I've ever had." A tear trickled from his eye as he realized that all the money in the world couldn't equal the love and laughter of such great friends.

Iggesund Botticelli
With Gustavo & Erica Fellini

"Hello, and welcome to Paradise Island, Cruzhead Jack," the orange man yelled out to the approaching giant. For weeks, Cruzhead Jack had been telling the Flying Mingling Brothers all about The Paradise Island Resort and Golf Club. Still nothing could really prepare them for the splendiferously amazing underwater club.

"Hello Uncle Iggy," Cruzhead Jack shouted back. All the while, the two Bubbas were spellbound by all the things they were seeing.

"Greetings, Cruzhead Jack and welcome," a soft, really beautiful voice said. It came from the same direction where Uncle Iggy was standing. The Bubbas couldn't see the woman standing behind the orange man. "Who have you brought with you, Jack?"

"A couple of Bubbas," Cruzhead Jack announced, as he approached the grand entrance. "This is Erica and Gustavo Fellini, and their uncle, Iggesund Boticelli."

"Hello there, how do you do?" the Bubbas said, and smiled at their friendly but unusual- looking hosts. "Nice to meet you."

"These are my new friends, the Flying Mingling Brothers. Bubba and Bubba," Cruzhead Jack said to them.

"Welcome, Bubbas," Erica's beautiful, soft voice said again. When

19

the boys got a closer look at Erica, they could see that her face was blue. You'd think she'd just been to the Rainbow Cafe, but had left before the food fight. Still, she had the warmest smile and nicest voice they'd ever heard.

"Thank you, Erica," they said in unison. "This is a really beautiful place you have here." As they were looking around, the Bubbas were trying to take everything in, they noticed that the two columns on each side of the entrance were clearly the work of Saint Augen Zauber. They were made of very colorful fish swimming up and down.

Gustavo Fellini

"Won't you please come in?" Erica said, and with a wave of her hand she welcomed the Bubbas in. Some very quick bellboys snapped up the guests bags and disappeared. The gigantic compound seemed to go on forever. The Paradise Hotel and clubhouse would barely fit into a large football stadium. The Double Bubbas were in complete awe. The reception was held in a magnificent room filled with more artwork than they'd ever seen. One painting that caught their eye in particular, was of their hosts. A fantastic family portrait of Uncle Iggy, Erica and someone they were just about to meet. Painted around the border of the painting were columns of Saint Augen Zauber's "up and down" swimming fish.

"Gee, what a lovely work of art," one of the Bubbas said to Erica.

"Oh, thank you Bubba" she said in that beautiful voice, and she blushed, and turned an even deeper shade of blue. "It was finished just in time for our upcoming Paradise Golf Tournament. Do you like it, really?"

"Never mind the painting, do you guys play golf?" Gustavo, Ericas husband said, interrupting. Without waiting for an answer, he said, "Come on fellows, let's go play a round." Before the boys could say "Okay," the automatic underwater golf carts had pulled up. Gustavo and Erica's cart was by far the most beautiful of all. It looked like it was made of solid gold, and it was pulled by two white dolphins. Everybody jumped into their carts and followed Gustavo and the Double Bubbas to the first tee. The Flying Mingling Brothers loved playing regular golf, but had no idea what it would be like to play underwater. Even in the world of the sea people, it's "ladies first," so Erica was the first to tee off. The balls moved in slow motion and it was funny to watch everybody swinging away. The Double Bubbas did very well, especially considering they were first-timers at under water golf. Gustavo won the round by one stroke, and was very impressed with the Flying Mingling Brothers.

"Would you fellows like to join our team, Bubbas" Gustavo asked

A fantastic painting of the Fellini family caught the Flying Mingling Brothers eyes.

them. "You could stay on until Saturday for the big tournament? What do you say?" The Flying Mingling Brothers answered immediately with a resounding **"Yes!"** That sounded great to them.

"We could use a couple of good partners," Erica said with a big smile and was already excited about having the Bubbas as partners on Saturday. "We've never won the tournament before, maybe with the Double Bubbas we have a chance."

"We'd love to help you in any way we can," the boys answered. "You can count on us." That night, back in their room, they were talking. "Hey Bubba, what do you think about the tournament? We don't know the first thing about this underwater golf."

"That's never stopped us before, Bubba. Let's win this thing for

Gustavo, Erica, and Uncle Iggy. What do you say?"

"We'll do it, Bubba. The word is 'mingle'."

"Mingle, it will be," and the two Bubbas laughed themselves to sleep that night. Without saying a word, they knew what that meant.

Saturday was there before they knew it, and it was time for the big tournament. The two Bubbas walked through the crowd, sizing up the competition. Everybody was dressed in their best golfing outfits, and

looking very sporty. The crowd was waiting for things to get started. Suddenly, a loud grumpy voice interrupted everything.

"Where are Gustavo and Erica Fellini?"

"Keep your pants on, they're coming," Uncle Iggy yelled back. He saw the two Bubbas in the crowd, and tapped them on their shoulders. "Good Morning, Bubbas," he said with a big orange smile. "Are you ready to win today?"

"You bet we are, Uncle Iggy," they answered with big smiles. "Where are Gustavo and Erica?"

But before he could answer, the two hosts pulled up in their spectacular golden golf cart, waving to the crowd.

"Let the game begin," Gustavo shouted out. The players were divided into teams of five. Uncle Iggy, Gustavo, Erica and the two Bubbas were a team. The game began and the Flying Mingling Brothers really got into the swing of things, and "mingled" all day. Besides playing very well, the boys told lots of funny stories. The extremely slow game allowed for plenty of jokes. They timed the punchlines of their jokes with the strokes of the opposing players. The two Bubbas would make faces, sneeze, hiccup and do almost anything to distract their opponents. Their clever offense was working, because everybody was missing shots, and not too happy about it. Still, the Flying Mingling Brothers weren't breaking any "official" under water golfing rules. Gustavo, Erica, and Uncle Iggy were delighted! Throughout the game, the Bubbas score was way ahead. After a while, their opponents got into the fun jokes and played along with the two Bubbas. It was a really great day.

That evening, a spectacular celebration feast was prepared for the winning team, and what a fantastic dinner it was! Afterward, Gustavo, Erica, and Uncle Iggy presented the Flying Mingling Brothers with a special gift. The beautiful painting they had admired when they first arrived. The Bubbas nearly lost their breath. For the first time ever, they were both speechless.

"Wow!" they finally spat out. "Uncle Iggy, Gustavo and Erica, we'll treasure this painting of you forever. Thank you, so very much!"

"Thank **you** for helping us win the tournament, Bubbas" Erica said in her lovely voice. "Will you come back next year, and help us win again, please?"

"Try'n stop us!" The two Bubbas were beaming.

"It was our pleasure, to have you two here, and you're welcome here any time," she said, kissing them both on the cheek. As she walked away, the two Bubbas thought, "I wonder whether we can ever find a love like Erica and Gustavo have?" Erica turned around, as if she had heard their thoughts. She winked at them and said, "Of course you will, boys. One day, I'll tell you how Gustavo and I met. It was all because of our friend dear King Valentine. Don't worry, Bubbas, love will find you."

Author's advice: If the reader is ever on a ship at sea and a golf ball should land at your feet, be sure to throw it right back into the water. Chances are you're passing over Paradise Island Resort and Golf Club and someone is looking in the deep seaweed for that ball.

King Valentine

* "King Valentine" was my very first oil painting.

Odam Googe

Odam Googe was a big man. He was a "Cruzhead" like Jack, but didn't work the boats. Odam had no sense of direction. He tried to be a cruzhead but quickly became unpopular with all the other cruisehead captains, because he could never find his way back to harbor. But there was something Odam Googe was really good at. He had an unbelievable talent for making the coolest costumes. When the Flying Mingling Brothers saw him the first time he was dressed in a spectacular huge black and white checkered suit, with the most amazing hat. His "hat" was a life-sized sandcastle made of real sand.

"Gee, Odam, that castle must be heavy!" they said simultaneously when they first met him. They'd never seen anybody dressed so bizarrely.

"Hello, Bubbas. Have you heard the one about the flying cow?" he asked, catching the boys a little off guard with his joke. Odam Googe had a secret ambition. He always dreamed of being king of the sea people. Every year he tried and tried to beat King Delectable in the coronation contest, but even he knew his jokes weren't very funny. Still, dreaming of winning, and trying out his jokes on people was his favorite thing to do. He would tell his latest jokes on anyone who would listen, hoping-looking for the BIG laugh.

"Why did the cow jump over the moon?" he asked the Bubbas next. The boys just shrugged their shoulders and shook their heads.

"To get to the 'udder' side."

There was no laughing, but the Double Bubbas did crack a little smile.

"We love your outfit, Odam. Did you make it yourself?" one of the Bubbas asked curiously. "Why, yes I did," Odam said with some pride. "Have you heard the one about the secret agent?"

"No," they said, this time looking at each other.

"Why did the secret agent cross the road?" There was no reply. "To catch the spy." he said with a big laugh. Once again, Odam Googe was the only person laughing. To change the subject, one of the Bubbas asked,

"Odam, have you ever been to the Mardi Gras in New Orleans?"

"No, what's Mardi Gras, Bubba?"

"It's only the biggest costume party in the world. It's usually held in

February or March every year," Bubba told him. "You should go sometime, they might make you "King of Mardi Gras," he said, not knowing anything about Odam's secret ambition.

"I could be king?" Odam asked with intense interest.

"Of course, why not? Every year the person with the best costume design is elected king. With one of your excellent costumes you could easily win!" the Bubbas said.

"Really?" Odam said. The boys could practically see his "wheels" spinning. "I'm going to make the best Mardi Gras costume anyone has ever seen! You'll see, Bubbas." Then, with a little bit of a worried look, he asked them, "Do I also have to be funny?"

"No, Odam no...don't worry, you just have to look good," the Double Bubbas said with a smile.

"Oh, perfect!" Odam said, and hurried home to get right to work. He spent the rest of the year making the most fantastic Mardi Gras costume ever.

The next time the Flying Mingling Brothers saw Odam Googe he was at the Mardi Gras in New Orleans. He was sitting in the middle of the street acting as a bridge for one of the big parades. The marchers and their floats were going up one shoulder and down the other. Odam had a gigantic crown on his head which read, "KING OF MARDI GRAS." Sitting on top of the crown was the most unbelievable float. It was a pumpkin filled with sea people. St. Augen Zauber had hypnotized some fish to be spokes for the wheels of the carriage, and a strange purple bird pulled the whole

Incredibly, Odam Googe had the real Man in the Moon napping atop the pumpkin filled with sea people on top of his head.

contraption. Incredibly, a real Man in the Moon napped atop the pumpkin. You'd have to see it to believe it. Odam Googe was a happiest fellow in the world, because he was finally KING, his dream fulfilled.

Because sea people can be on land for only twenty-four hours, Odam was glad the party ended at midnight. He said good-bye to everybody, especially to the Flying Mingling Brothers.

"Ooooohhhhh Bubbas," he yelled out. "Come over here and let me give you a big hug! If I hadn't met you guys I'd never be King of Mardi Gras. How can I ever thank you?" He nearly squeezed the life out of his two friends with his huge hug.

"You already have, Your Highness," the two Bubbas said with a big grin. "Just please say hello to all our friends down in the sea world, Odam, especially Cruise Head Jack. We miss them so," they said, salty tears squirting from their eyes.

"O.K. Bubas, bye-bye for now! I promise I will say hello to everybody for you, and I'll be back next year, when I plan to reign again as King of Mardi Gras.

Smilin' Sam

The Flying Mingling Brothers did not like the cold weather. Every winter they'd head south to a tropical island, where the weather was always perfect. One time, they visited an island so small it didn't even have a name. It was there they met a practical joker named Smilin' Sam. Smilin' Sam was the island's sandwich maker, and for some reason no local people ever ate at his cozy little beach restaurant. He made sandwiches only for visiting tourists.

The two Bubbas had just arrived on the island and were strolling along the beach, when they spotted Smilin' Sam's colorful little sandwich shack under the coconut trees.

"Hey look, Bubba,

Smilin' Sam's sandwiches cost only twenty-five cents.

Food! Let's go!"

"I'm with ya, Bubba, what are we waiting for?" They walk over and right away make themselves comfortable in the large bamboo chairs. On every table and hanging over the counter are signs that say:

The boys are thrilled. Sandwiches for twenty-five cents. What a deal. "I'm starvin', Bubba!"

"Me, too. Let's order a bunch." A friendly little fat man comes over to take their order and says in a deep husky voice, "Hello fellows, my name is Sam, but some folks call me Smilin' Sam. Welcome to my restaurant. How many would you like? The sandwiches are always fresh and look delicious!"

"Hi Sam! What a beautiful place you have here." the boys answer. "We're the Flying Mingling Brothers, Bubba and Bubba. We're starving, would you please bring us a dozen of your sandwiches?"

"Sure Bubbas, something to drink?" asks Sam.

"How 'bout two bottles of water?"

"That'll be five dollars, please," Smiling Sam says with a smile and presents the bill.

"How odd," the two Bubbas think. "We're the only customers in the place and he wants his money before we've even seen the sandwiches?" Still, they happily pay him and even slip him an extra dollar tip.

"Thank you very much gentlemen," Sam says with a smile, and goes back to his kitchen. Smilin' Sam makes his luscious-looking sandwiches with lettuce, tomato, and lots of his "secret sauce" on fresh-baked bread. He knows how to make them very quickly and has a platter piled high in just a few minutes.

"Bon appetite, Bubbas!" Smilin' Sam says, with a giggle putting the sandwiches down in front of them. The boys can't believe their luck. There are enough sandwiches there to last maybe a week. Delighted, they take their first bite. They chew once or twice before they realize that the "secret sauce" is a mix of onions, pickles, a little mayonnaise and a lot of SAND!

"PTUIEEEEE!" They spit out the awful bite of sandy sandwich. "YUCK!" they say in unison and are glad they have that dollar water.

They quickly rinse out their mouths and are about to say something nasty to Sam, when they hear "giggle, giggle, giggle." The giggles are coming from behind every coconut tree all around the restaurant where children are peeking out and laughing at the unhappy Bubbas. They've been watching the Bubbas the whole time and are busting out with laughter. Apparently, the favorite thing for the island children to do, is to watch Smilin' Sam play his little tricks on the tourists. Sam is never mean-spirited about it and it is always in good fun. Everyone is laughing, everyone that is, except the two Bubbas, but Smilin' Sam's laugh can be heard over everybody's.

"HA, HA, HA, HA," he bellows. "Sorry boys, HA, HA, HA, HA, but down here, on this island, it is our custom to play practical jokes on newcomers. HA, HA, HA, HA." He even offers them a refund, but of course the boys refuse. The Double Bubbas actually love being Sam's latest victim.

"Good one, Sam!" They say loudly, each with a mile-wide smile. "We should have known," one of the Bubbas says. "If it looks too good to be true, it always is."

They thank Smilin' Sam for the fun and join the children for some games of hide and seek, and hide behind a coconut tree to wait for the next victims fall into Smilin' Sam's little sand trap. It was a fun day, but the Flying Mingling Brothers never again ate at Smilin' Sam's.

Dogtown Molly Brown's favorite
Kitties. Garden Kitty, Martini Kitty
and the Sun and Moon Kitties.

Paddy O'Shea

Dogtown is a small, beautiful neighborhood in St. Louis, Missouri, famous for its excellent restaurants, none of which serve dogmeat. It is also famous for it's big St. Patrick's Day parade and festivities. This year, on the day before St. Patrick's Day, the Flying Mingling Brothers stop in to visit their good friend, Dogtown Molly Brown. When they pull up to the house her dogs start to bark like crazy. The kitties are very curious too. "Who can that be?" she wonders aloud. She opens the door and is delighted to see that it is her good friends the Double Bubbas.

"Hello, Dogtown Molly Brown," they say in unison.

"Hello, Bubbas!" she

Paddy O'Shea was a very talented singer and harp player

yells out, but is drowned out by all the barking and howling of her animals. Jumping up on the two Bubbas, the dogs, the kitties, and Molly smother the Flying Mingling Brothers with hugs, licks, and kisses. When everything settles and the animals calm down she says, "I'm so glad you've come! We're gonna have so much fun tomorrow! St. Patrick's Day is the biggest day of the year in Dogtown. As usual, you boys got here just in time for dinner. I made a special Irish feast." Their mouths water at the smell of corned beef and cabbage cooking. The Bubbas help set the table, and then Molly serves up the most delicious Irish feast they've ever eaten. Afterward, over a cup of coffee, she asks them, "Have you ever heard the story of Paddy O' Shea?" "He's the one who started the tradition of our Dogtown St. Patrick's Day celebrations."

"No, I don't believe we have," says one Bubba, and the other adds politely, "but we'd love to hear it, Molly."

"Okay then." She takes a sip of her

DogTown
MOLLY
BROWN

coffee and begins. "Many years ago, Paddy O' Shea moved to Dogtown from Ireland when he was only nine and a half years old." she began. He loved his new home in America and the new neighborhood just fine, but in his heart he always missed his beloved Ireland. Even as a young boy, Paddy was a very talented singer and harp player. He sang Irish songs as his way of staying in touch with his homeland. People loved his Irish songs and always showed their appreciation by dropping a coin or two into young Paddy's hat. He made a lot of money playing his music this way. Paddy played in Dogtown and all around St. Louis for many years, and over time he saved up a small fortune in coins.

Paddy O' Shea's favorite day of the year without a doubt, was St. Patrick's Day. He lived for it. Every year Paddy could hardly wait for March 17th. One year it snowed and snowed for several days prior to the big day. Dogtown and all of St. Louis came to a complete standstill. On the night before St. Patrick's Day, Paddy was standing in the window looking out at the falling snow, a river of tears streaming down his face. "There will be no St. Patrick's Day this year," he cried to himself. Because he was so upset he couldn't even eat his supper. Paddy went straight to bed that night and cried himself to sleep. While he was in a deep, deep, sleep, a little green leprechaun appeared to him.

"Poor, pitiful Patrick Seamus O' Shea," the little person said to Paddy. "You should be ashamed! Feelin' sorry for yerself, are ya laddy?" the leprechaun asked with a sneer. Then he said, "Saint Patrick sent me with this message for you." The leprechaun handed Paddy a small, sealed envelope addressed to "Patrick Seamus O' Shea." Paddy opened the letter and it read, "GIVE IT BACK AND I WILL COME." He looked up to ask what the note meant, but the little green man was already gone. Paddy woke up, saying out loud, "Give WHAT back, he wondered?" then fell back to sleep. The snow finally stopped sometime during the long night. Paddy woke up the next morning wearing a big smile. He had figured out what the letter from St. Patrick meant. "I know what I'll do," he said. I'll give back all the coins I've been saving all these years. The people of St. Louis, and especially Dogtown have been so kind to me. I can think of nothing I'd rather do with my savings," he thought happily.

So, right after lunch that day, Paddy Seamus O' Shea stuffed his pockets full of coins and loaded up his toboggan with bags and bags of money he'd pulled out of secret hiding places. The last thing he loaded on top was his trusty harp. He pulled the heavy sled into the heart of Dogtown and set up at his favorite corner. All day long he played his harp and sang songs at the top of his lungs. Instead of his usual plastic shamrocks, Paddy passed out bag after bag of money.

By mid-afternoon, Dogtown had crowds like no one had ever seen. Everybody had forgotten the snow. They were dancing and singing along with Paddy and having the time of their lives.

Most of all though, they loved all the free money. Needless to say, Patrick Seamus O' Shea easily won the "Most Popular Person" award that day. Paddy finally threw away his last coins and shouted, "HAPPY ST. PATRICK'S DAY, EVERYBODY!" It was the happiest he'd ever felt.

"You're a saint, Paddy," someone yelled from the crowd, and everyone echoed. "You're a saint, Paddy!" Poor little Paddy turned bright red, and said very shyly, "No I'm not, but the real Saint Patrick did tell me he would come today." He continued to look around for him, as he had been all afternoon. "Too bad," he thought, "St. Patrick would've enjoyed all the fun." The party finally came to an end and Paddy finally went home completely happy. To his surprise, sitting in his living room, was the little green leprechaun.

"Cry baby Patrick Seamus O' Shea," he said in a nicer voice this time. "So, how was your day then, laddy?" said the little green man.

"Oh, Mr. Leprechaun, I'm so sorry I was such a cry baby the other night. Today was the best day of my whole life! The only thing that could' ve made it better, was if Saint Patrick had come," he said a little sadly, then he added quickly, "it sure was a great day though. God Bless Ireland and all the Irish. Erin Go Braugh!"

The little green leprechaun smiled and winked at Paddy O'Shea. "Think about it, Paddy....." he said and just like that, he was gone.

"Would you care for some more coffee?" Molly asks the two startled Bubbas. They are both so absorbed in her story, they've lost track of where they are.

"Thank you for the lovely story, Molly. We can't wait to meet Paddy O' Shea tomorrow," Bubba says smiling. "More coffee would be great."

The next day Dogtown is the place to be. There's a huge St. Patrick's Day parade and everyone is singing, dancing, and having a grand ole' time, but the Flying Mingling Brothers never see Paddy O' Shea. At Molly's house that night, they ask, "what a great St. Patrick's Day party, Molly, and thanks for inviting us. It sure was fun, but we never did get to see Paddy O' Shea, did you?" Dogtown Molly Brown smiles at the two Bubbas and says, "Think about it boys.....Think about it.....Goodnight, Bubbas."

Chet Blankenship

Everyone knows that the hotdogs in Chicago are especially delicious. Whenever the Flying Mingling Brothers drive through there, they always stop for some. One beautiful summer evening, as they are passing through the Windy City Bubba interrupts the silence.

"How 'bout a dog, Bubba?" he says in a big, fat southern drawl.

"Yeah Bubba, a dog and a shake would really hit the spot." They pull off the highway and stop at themost famous hotdog stand in Chicago, Hot Dog Charlie's. While waiting in line, they meet a scrawny young man.

"Excuse me," the young man says to the Flying Mingling Brothers. "Do you have any aspirin? I think I have a headache coming on and a couple of aspirin just might curb it," he says very seriously. The two Bubbas feel bad for the fellow and say, "Sorry buddy, we don't have any medicines with us, not even aspirin."

"Oh, that's okay," he says. "You know, come to think of it, I have some aspirin right here." He digs through his shirt pockets and victoriously pulls out two tablets. Before the two Bubbas can blink, he has gulped them down. "My name is Chet Blankenship," he says, "and my hobby is collecting baseball cards. Would you guys like to come over and see my collection?" He puts his hand on his head any says, "Excuse me fellows, would either of you have an aspirin? I think I feel a headache coming on. A couple of aspirin might curb it."

"Sorry Chet, we don't have any," one of the Bubbas says, giving the other Bubba a look.

"Oh, that's Okay," Chet says, "I just realized that I have some right here in my pocket." Just like that, he pops two more pills into his mouth and swallows them quickly.

"Wow," one of the Bubbas says, "Poor guy, he must feel a whopper of a headache coming on."

"Yeah, too bad." They feel genuinely sorry for him. "Listen Chet, we'd love to see your collection, but we've got to go. We're on our way to a big music festival in Detroit and we're running a little late."

"Ooooooooh…….Can I come along, please? I've never been to a music festival. Please?" He puts his hand suddenly to his head, saying, "Excuse me, but do either of you have an aspirin? I think I feel a headache coming on." They don't answer this time, instead they just shake their

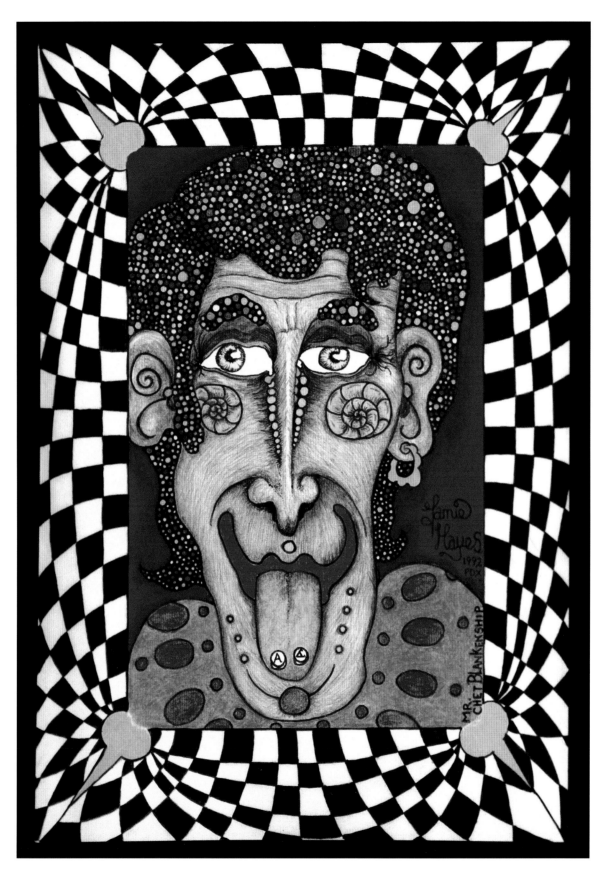

"I think I feel a headache coming on."

45

heads. Chet pops two more pills.

"Chet's a hypochondriac," Bubba whispers to Bubba. "Maybe we should take him away on a little road trip to Detroit for the weekend." The Flying Mingling Brothers are softies with big hearts. The two Bubbas smile at Chet Blankenship and then, just as if they had rehearsed it, they break into song. It is almost like the spirit of Big Daddy Boudreaux takes over.

"It's time to go,

we're going to a festival.

To see and hear the show,

you can come and get away,

but those headaches and aspirin,

have got to stay."

"Yeah," Chet yells out. "Let's go! But first, can we stop off at my house for a minute? I need to pick up some clothes and a toothbrush. I live right around the corner."

"Okay, but let's hurry," Bubba mumbles around a mouth full of one of those delicious hotdogs. They drive over to Chet's house, figuring to stop in for only a minute, but when they see Chet's baseball collection, the Flying Mingling Brothers forget all about time. "Wow!" the two Bubbas say, "Wow!" They are overwhelmed with room after room full of baseball memorabilia. "Chet must have every baseball card that's ever been printed," Bubba says to Bubba. The house is like a private baseball museum. Jokingly, one of them asks, "so Chet, I take it you really love baseball?"

"Yes, I really do. I just love collecting all this stuff, and have been collecting since I was a little boy. It was my Dad who got me started. Excuse me, but do either of you have an aspirin? I think I feel a headache coming on." The boys don't answer him and just say, "Go grab your things Chet, we have to go! Don't forget to FORGET your aspirins."

The three pile into the van and drive off to the festival and have a fabulous weekend. The music is great and they all mingle, dance, and have a wonderful time. Monday morning they are driving back to Chicago and one of the Bubbas says to Chet, "Hey, Chet Blankenship, do you realize you haven't asked us for a single aspirin all weekend?"

"You know, you're right Bubba! Excuse me," he says with a big smile, "but do you have an aspirin? I think I have a headache coming on..." Everybody laughs. Then Chet yells out, "STOP THE CAR!" The Double Bubbas are perplexed. Bubba pulls over and Chet jumps out.

"You know boys, the only thing waiting for me at home, is a headache and my baseball stuff. This time I'm taking the slow road. I'm gonna walk the rest of the way. Goodbye, Flying Mingling Brothers," he says with a happy face. A tiny tear rolls down Chet's cheek as he says, "thank you so much for everything from the bottom of my heart, Bubbas."

"Bye-bye Chet. Take care of yourself and please keep on forgetting those headaches! Remember, music is the best medicine!" The two Bubbas leave the happy-looking Chet on the side of the road, with the music blaring from their radio as they drive off to their next adventure.

New Orleans Music

Big Daddy Boudreaux is the most famous singer and band leader in New Orleans. His band is called, 'Big Daddy and the Big Easy' is made up of the greatest musicians in the city, who do something no other band can do. To play in Big Daddy's band, every member has to be able to play their instrument on top of their head. (All except the harmonica players, who stuff the whole thing into their mouths.) With their hands free, they can snap their fingers to the beat, and also play drums or other rhythm instruments at the same time.

The Flying Mingling Brothers meet Big Daddy Boudreaux at a party one afternoon in the heart of the French Quarter, and it doesn't take long for three to mingle. The two Bubbas walk right up to Big Daddy Boudreau and introduce themselves. When the two Bubbas start talking with Big Daddy, they are surprised to find that he answers every question with a song.

"Hello, Big Daddy, we're the Flying Mingling Brothers, Bubba and Bubba. It's so nice to meet you! We've heard all about you and your red hot band. How's everything going with you and the band?"

Big Daddy Boudreaux's wide smile stretches even wider. He winks at the two Bubbas, and says, "why, thank you for asking." He starts snapping his fingers to a beat and begins to sing.

"My daddy's fine,

My mama's fine,

My sister's fine,

My brother's fine.

My grand-mamie and pappie are fine,

Everybody on my street is fine,

The band feels fine, and

Lord knows, I feel fine."

Even before Big Daddy Boudreaux is finished singing his answer, the Double Bubbas are grinning from ear to ear. They have never heard anyone answer a question that way before. The boys keep asking him all sorts of things. For every question they have, he makes up a song for an answer. The Bubbas love it.

After a while, Big Daddy looks at his watch and says, "Wow, Bubbas, I'm late, for a very important date, and I can't be slow, 'cause I gotta go!" He slips the Bubbas a couple of free tickets to the show later that night, and as he heads toward the door, he starts singing:

"I hope I see you all later,

at our music show.

Now, my friends,

I hate to leave,

But it's time for me to go."

And with that, Big Daddy is out the door.

That night, the Double Bubbas get all dressed up for the big show.

50

The boys are sporting very stylish outfits, including their favorite red dancing shoes. They're ready for anything!

"Let's go dance, Bubba. The girls are sure to be out tonight, so let's not keep them waiting," Bubba says with a laugh, and just like that the two are out the door.

At midnight, the lights in the nightclub go out and the sounds of drums and tamborines fill the room. Big Daddy's band starts playing a kind of music the Bubbas have never heard before. Without even knowing it,

Big Daddy's band starts playing a kind of music the Bubbas have never heard before.

The Harmonica Club of New Orleans sometimes performs with Big Daddy Boudreaux and his band.

their red shoes start moving to the beat of the drums. Slowly, the lights come back on. Everybodys waving their hands in the air, and dancing to the magical, rhythmic sounds of Big Daddy and the Big Easy. The band jams on and on until the wee hours, and the Flying Mingling Brothers mingle until the last note is played. Afterward, they go backstage to thank Big Daddy, and to tell him how much they enjoyed the show. He sees the Flying Mingling Brothers coming and smiles. "Hey, Bubbas, how'd you enjoy the show?"

Without missing a beat, the two Bubbas look at each other and start snapping their fingers. They break into a little song for Big Daddy:

"The show was fine,
we had a real good time.
Thanks, Big Daddy Boudreaux,
we'll see you next time...!"

Everybody busts out laughing, and the Bubbas feel like they've known Big Daddy all their lives.

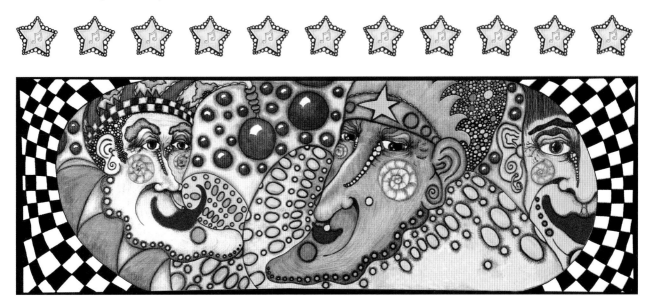

The Flying Mingling Brothers had seen Gumbalino's noodle hat many times, but until that day they'd never seen it doing it's thing, making spaghetti noodles.

Gumbalino

Frederico "Guiseppe" Gumbalino is a great Louisiana chef, and everyone loves his famous noodle hat. His hat is important, because it makes the "Bayou Noodles" he sells at the New Orleans French Market.

The Flying Mingling Brothers were helping their friend Gumbalino at his "Bayou Noodle and Spice" stand one Saturday, when to their surprise he said, "Bubbas, why don't you come out to my home on the bayou tomorrow? I'll cook up a little something, and we'll have a party. What do you say?"

"Why sure, Gumbalino!" The two Bubbas never pass up a free meal. They were especially thrilled, because they'd finally be able to sample some of Gumbalino's cooking and see his house on the bayou they'd heard so much about. "We'll see you there! What time should we show up?"

"Come early and stay late," he answers with a big smile.

"Okay then, see you tomorrow." The two Bubbas say, and head home for a good night's sleep.

The next morning the boys drive out of New Orleans and way down deep into the bayou. They get lost, as they nearly always do, because the Bubbas never use a map, but after a few wrong turns they finally find Gumbalino's house. What a fantastic house it is too! It's an old plantation with a circular, tree-lined drive and a huge yard full of animals. As they pull up the drive, the animals go berserk and scatter in every direction. Apparently, Gumbalino doesn't get many visitors, so strangers really frighten them. The chickens seem especially skittish. They run in long, funny looking strides, flapping their wings like crazy. The roosters lead the way, cock-a-doodling at the top of their lungs. The Bubbas laugh as they pull up to the house. Gumbalino comes out on the oversize front porch, and stands under a large paper banner he has made which reads,

"Welcome Flying Mingling Brothers."

"Howdy Bubbas," he shouts and waves. "Never mind those critters. They'll calm down soon enough. All except the chickens, they'll probably keep runnin' 'til you leave!" he says, laughing. "I'm so glad you made it, Bubbas," Gumbalino continues. "I've been meaning to have you come out here long before this. Welcome, and come on in! Ma maison, et tu maison," (my house, is your house,) he says in perfect Cajun French.

The Bubbas smile up at him and say, "Hey there, Gumbalino, what a beautiful place you have here."

"Thanks Bubbas," and with some pride adds, "the house has been in my family for over two hundred years, and the spice garden over there even longer. Come on in, I'll cook up some Bayou Noodle Spaghetti and brew up some iced tea."

The house, decorated in an old-fashioned style, is full of all sorts of interesting things. The Bubbas' absolutely favorite room in the house is the kitchen. Gumbalino really has it all decked out. There are hundreds of hooks holding pots and pans, bunches of garlic, peppers in every color, and every imaginable spice. Everything seems to have its place, even though the kitchen is stuffed completely full.

The Flying Mingling Brothers had seen Gumbalino's noodle hat many times, but until that day, they'd never seen it doing its thing---making noodles. As Gumbalino begins to cook, the noodles come curling out of the top of his hat. He breaks them off when they get to just the right length. Then, he straightens and stacks the newly made noodles on th kitchen counter top. Gumbalino dumps all sorts of things into a huge pot on the stove. "I got this recipe from my great, great, great, great-grand-mother and something tells me you're gonna like it."

"It sure smells heavenly, Gumbalino!" The Bubbas exclaim, their mouths watering and point to a very interesting painting they see hanging over the kitchen table, "Hey, who's that?" they ask.

"Oh," Gumbalino says, and smiles, "that's my great, great, great, great-grandfather, "Gumba" Gumbalino. He was the first in our family to come over from Italy to Louisiana, in fact, he built this house. Everybody loved Grandpa Gumba, he was known as the friendliest man in the bayou."

"Wow, Gumbalino, you look just like your grandpa Gumba!" they say, amazed at the family resemblance. Gumbalino blushes with pride and puts the final ingredients into his sauce.

"This has got to cook a while. So, how'd you like to go on the grand tour?" Gumbalino gets up, and heads outside. The two Bubbas follow him out to his propeller boat. Everybody piles in and they proceed to drive around the swamp all afternoon. It was like a long, loud, and really wild roller coaster ride. The Bubbas have never had so much fun.

When they finally arrive back at Gumbalino's house everybody is starving. They follow the smell back to the kitchen, their mouths watering. Gumbalino boils up the noodles, and after a little while dinner is served.

"Bon appetite, boys," Gumbalino says, as they sit down to eat. There are several "Bites Of Silence," before one of the Bubbas can utter a sound. "Yausa!," one of them says breathlessly. Together, they sing out, **"It's soooooooooooooooo delicious!** How do you cook like this, Gumbalino?"

Gumbalino's blue eyes sparkle and he just smiles. The two Bubbas eat so much spaghetti, they nearly pop! After dinner, they ask, "Hey, Gumbalino, Bubba and I are writing our memoirs. It's going to be a children's book. Do you think you might share your "Bayou Noodle Spaghetti" recipe with us? We'd love to put it in our book.

"Of course, Bubbas. I'd love Bayou Noodle Spaghetti to be part of your book, that would be great." He tells them in great detail how he makes his delicious spaghetti. Here is exactly how you can make it yourselves!

Gumbalino's Bayou Noodle Spaghetti

3 tablespoons olive oil

1 large onion

2 chopped celery ribs with leaves

1 chopped green pepper

2 cloves garlic

1 28-ounce can crushed tomatoes

1 12-ounce can tomato paste

1 tablespoon Louisiana-style hot sauce

1 teaspoon sea salt

1/2 teaspoon brown sugar

1 sprig parsley

1 sprig basil

1 bay leaf

1 pound sweet Italian sausage, pan fried

1 pound mozzerella cheese, shredded

1 pound Gumbalino's Bayou Noodles, cooked al dente (if you can't find
   Gumbalino's noodles you can substitute regular spaghetti noodles)

Saute onions, celery, green pepper, and garlic in olive oil. Add tomatoes, tomato paste, hot sauce, and seasonings. Cook gently, uncovered, for about 45 minutes until mixture is thick. Preheat oven to 375 degrees. Put cooked noodles in a 4-quart casserole dish, top with 1/2 cup of shredded cheese, next layer tomato sauce, sausage, and remaining cheese. Bake 25 minutes, or until golden brown and bubbly.

After he finishes telling the boys the recipe, he adds, "Its very important to be in a good mood when you make Bayou Noodle Spaghetti. It adds a nice flavor, and besides, all food tastes better when it is made with love, laughter and a little music."

A full moon comes up over the Bayou, and it's time for the Bubbas to get back to New Orleans. They thank Gumbalino for a teriffic day, and especially for the Bayou Noodle Spaghetti recipe.

"Hurry back, Bubbas!" Gumbalino says, waving good-bye. "Let's do it again soon! Y'all drive safely, ya' hear? See you Saturday at the French Market."

Just as the two are pulling away, they catch a glimpse of the chickens still running in ragged circles. The Flying Mingling Brothers laugh all the way home.

Peter the Pianoeater

Peter the Pianoeater is the most famous musician who ever came from New Orleans. Even as a little boy he showed a remarkable musical talent. He could sing and dance even before he could walk and talk. He mastered any instrument he picked up. Most of all, though, he loved to play the piano. Peter is the best piano player the Flying Mingling Brothers have ever heard, but the way he plays is what makes his music so special.

Musical little Peter had been a popular kid in his neighborhood. Everybody liked him. One day, when Peter was about twelve years old, he had an idea. "I only wish I could take my piano with me wherever I go. Hey, I know!" he thought. "Maybe there's some way I could swallow a small piano."

No one told him it wasn't possible, so right then, he started to figure out how he could swallow a piano. First, he experimented with baseballs, then softballs, even footballs. He kept putting larger and larger objects into his mouth and walking around that way for days. The neighbours began to worry when they saw him stuffing a basketball into his mouth one day.

"Hey Peter," Mrs. Flathead, one of his nosey neighbours shouted. "What's up with the basketball in your mouth?" But since he had a basketball in his mouth, he couldn't answer. He didn't want to tell her what he was doing anyway. He just kept practicing and practicing, until one morning he woke up and knew....**THIS IS THE DAY!**

Peter had saved up his money and bought the perfect little piano. It was sitting in his livingroom, ready. He got up and walked right over to it, picked it up and, in one giant gulp, swallowed the whole thing. Muffled sounds of "plunk, clink, kerplunk, bing-bong" came through his new teeth as the little piano rumbled around in his stomach. Peter smiled and was very happy with himself. Where his teeth once were, there is now a keyboard. When he smiles, the keys glisten and he can play them right there, in his mouth. In the beginning it was a little difficult to move around, but now he can play, dance, and sing, all at the same time. Peter has become the talk of the town, and people come from everywhere to see and hear him play.

The Flying Mingling Brothers are good friends with Peter the

Pianoeater and have seen many of his performances. In fact, they were there the night he found his little Miss Irie. It was at the "Doodle Doo Dance Club," in Dalton, Louisiana. Peter was playing to a sellout crowd when he spotted her. Like magic, their eyes met and he never saw anybody else that night. It was love at first sight. Every song he played from that moment on was only for Miss Irie.

They married a month later and have lived happily ever since. Over the years their true love has made twenty-seven children, all of them musically gifted---but none can swallow a piano. They are very proud of their father Peter, the world's one and only pianoeater.

The End

Jamie Hayes was born in Greencastle, Indiana, in 1951. After growing up in Graz, Austria, Jamie spent many years travelling the world as a professional artist and singer-songwriter. He lived in Holland, Mexico, Morocco, Bali, Indonesia, Thailand, finally winding up back in New Orleans Louisiana, the place he considers home.

Jamie's artistic background is in scrimshaw, the indiginous North American folk-art of engraving fossilized ivory. After 23 years as a scrimshander and taking home numerous first-place awards, Jamie "retired" from that carreer. Following that, there was a 10-year period of searching the world for fossils and mineral specimens, selling them at mineral shows. Along with Mike Clanton of Birmingham, Alabama, the two best friends, who called themselves "Bubba and Bubba," became the Flying Mingling Brothers. They travelled, had loads of fun and mingled together all over the world.

Sadly, Mike, a.k.a. Bubba, died April, 1, 1992, in Guatemala, and it was from this tragic experience that Jamie's art was born. Jamie's "therapy" was to draw, paint and write these stories, which are (very) loosly based on their real life experiences. They helped him get through the loss of his best friend, Bubba. This book was a five year labor of love, and each picture represents hundreds of hours of work. An interesting fact is that Jamie is extremely color-blind. The hair on his characters, small, colorful cirlcles, represent color-blind tests. The sea shells on their cheeks represent ammonites---fossilized seashells.

Jamie is proudest of his wife Pam, and their 15 month old son Julian, the joy in his life. They live with their two cats in the French Quarter of New Orleans.

The wait is over.

"Up In The Air

with the

Flying Mingling Brothers"

Now available, Jamie's new children's book.

To order a copy go to:

jamiehayes.com

(opening page of "Up In The Air")

CAPTAIN CHESTER SIMO

It all happened one after noon when the two Bubbas were cruising along a country road somewhere. Suddenly their "cutter" began to sputter, and came to a stop right smack in the middle of nowhere. The boys had recently bought this rather ugly-looking car for 100 dollars, and then cut the roof off. After this haircut, the automobile dinosaur looked kind of cool, and it ran just fine. At least until the moment when the motor started to cough, and they had to pull over to the side of the road. The wrong place to foolishly run out of gasoline. The Bubba who was driving was playing his famous gas gauge game, only this time he didn't quite make it to the next gas station.

Just as the two began blaming each other for running out of gas, AND for not having a map, they heard the sound of a motor coming from above them. They couldn't believe what they saw. Hovering overhead was a gigantic blimp. Hanging from its side, was the longest ladder the boys had ever seen. It looked like an invitation to them, so they climbed upward, one Bubba after the other. The next thing they heard was the motor being turned off, and shortly after that, the sound of a man's voice coming from the blimp.........